Dear Reader,

Do you sometimes need to relax after a long and hard day? To really have fun, chill out and laugh a little bit? If you do, then you have come to the right place, because this is exactly what this book is all about.

You can see this impolite coloring book as a small corner of paradise where you can come anytime to have fun, laugh and really just chill the fuck out. Irreverent as hell, this hilarious and vulgar, yet beautiful coloring book has been created so you can celebrate the artist within in a fun and spontaneous way.

On your irreverent journey, you will find cute animals, leaves and abstract patterns uniquely articulated around swear words and expressions such as 'Dumbass', 'You're such a dick', and many others.

Every month, I send out free coloring pages to my e-mail community. Feel free to join us at: **colorfulswearing.com/community**

Find a cosy corner and enjoy the book!

Alex Fleming

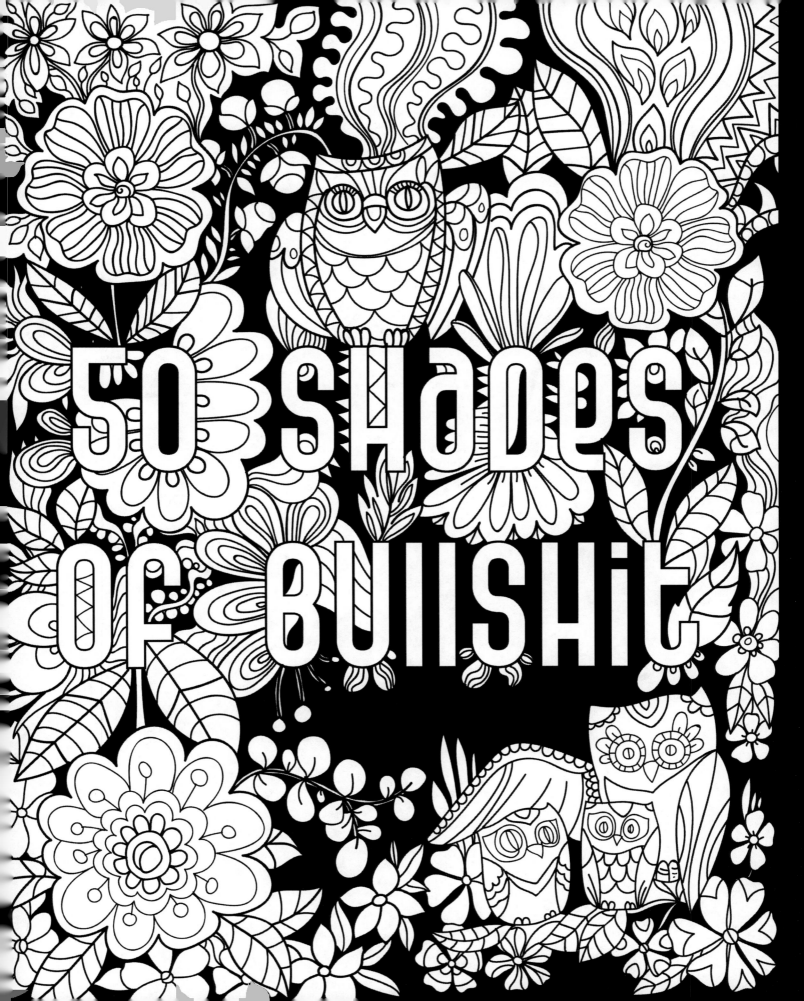

PRINT THIS BOOK

Download this entire book in printable PDF format at:
colorfulswearing.com/PDF50

GET MY PREVIOUS BOOK FOR FREE

Every month, I send out new sweary coloring pages for free to all my e-mail sweary community. Join us now and instantly receive my last book for free in printable PDF format:
colorfulswearing.com/freebook

CONNECT

I run a Facebook page where I share coloring pages, run contests and give you updates on my upcoming books. You can join me at:
facebook.com/colorfulswearing

There is also an awesome private sweary Facebook group you can join, with artists and colorists from everywhere. We share free pages to color, run giveaways and contests. You can join the group here:
facebook.com/groups/swearywords

And feel free to add me as a friend on Facebook. I enjoy sharing and connecting with all of you, artists and colorists alike, and I would be more than happy to connect with you too. You can add me here:
facebook.com/alexfleming123

Would you be kind enough to review my book?

Reviews are my oxygen. Without your feedbacks, I would not be able to improve this book, nor would I be able to constantly make my new books better.

Reviews are also what make people buy my books. In fact, you probably read some reviews before purchasing this one.

So if you enjoyed this book, please take 5 minutes to post an honest review on Amazon. I would really, really appreciate.

With love,
Alex F.

Copyright 2016 © Colorful Swearing
In no way is it legal to reproduce, duplicate or transmit any parts of this document in either electronic means or in printed format unless with written consent from the publisher.